NO SMALL PLANS

by
Gabrielle Lyon
Devin Mawdsley
Kayce Bayer
Chris Lin
Deon Reed

MMXVII

CHICAGO ARCHITECTURE FOUNDATION

No Small Plans

By Gabrielle Lyon with Eyes of the Cat Illustration:
Devin Mawdsley, Kayce Bayer, Chris Lin and Deon Reed

Credits

Gabrielle Lyon: Creative Director, Writer, Editor
Devin Mawdsley: Pencil & Ink Chapters 1, 2, 3; Color Chapter 3
Kayce Bayer: Color Chapters 1, 2, 3 & Burnham Interludes 1, 2, 3; Image Editor; Writing, Research
Chris Lin: Pencil & Ink Burnham Interludes 1, 2, 3; Color Chapters 1, 2, 3; Lettering; Cover Art
Deon Reed: Maps 1, 2, 3; Color Chapters 1, 2, 3; Cover Art

Published by Chicago Architecture Foundation, Chicago, Illinois

© 2017 by Chicago Architecture Foundation. All rights reserved.
Printed in the United States of America
Chicago printing
ISBN: 978-0-9973615-1-3
Library of Congress Control Number: 2017941278

Every copy of *No Small Plans* sold enables CAF to give a copy away for free.
Bulk and educator rates are available by emailing **groupsales@architecture.org**.

architecture.org/NoSmallPlans

CHICAGO ARCHITECTURE FOUNDATION

The **Chicago Architecture Foundation** (CAF) is a nonprofit organization dedicated to inspiring people to discover why design matters. As an educational organization, CAF offers tours, programs, exhibitions, field trips, curricula and online tools that are part of a learning journey for all ages. Proceeds from CAF's tours and store, as well as grants, sponsorships and donations, support this educational mission. For more information, please visit **architecture.org** or call **312.922.3432.**

No Small Plans and the Meet Your City initiative are made possible in part by the generous support of

NO SMALL PLANS

CHAPTER 1:
THE PAST, 1928

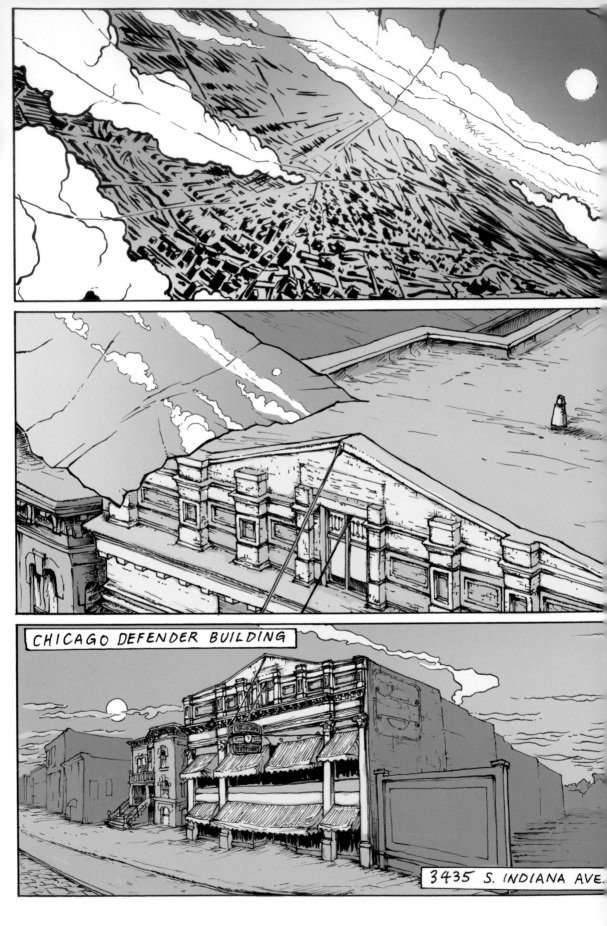

7

8

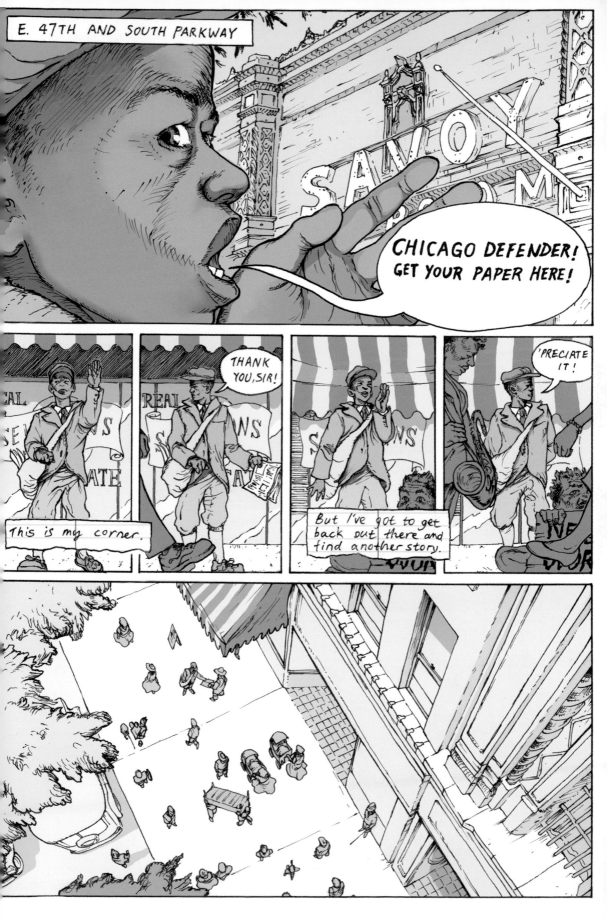

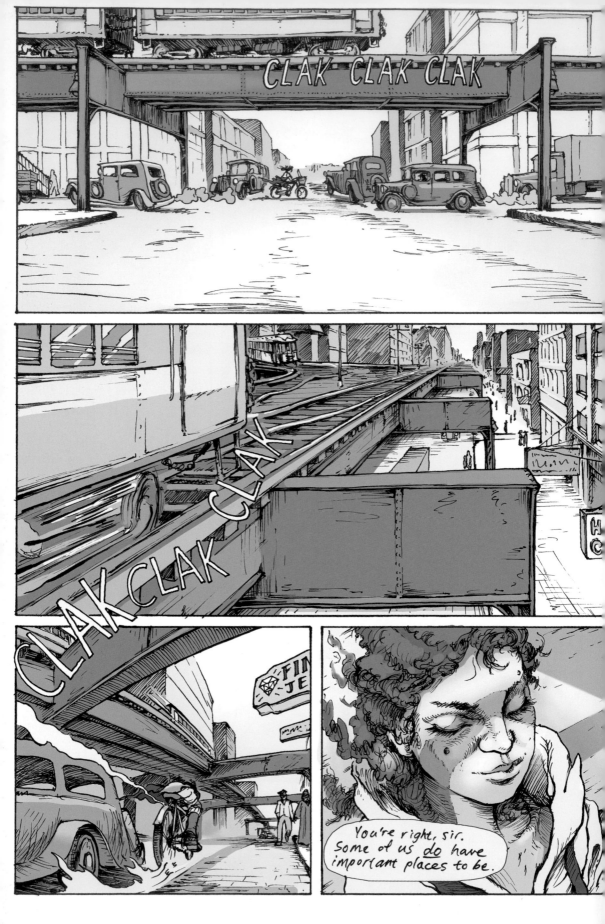

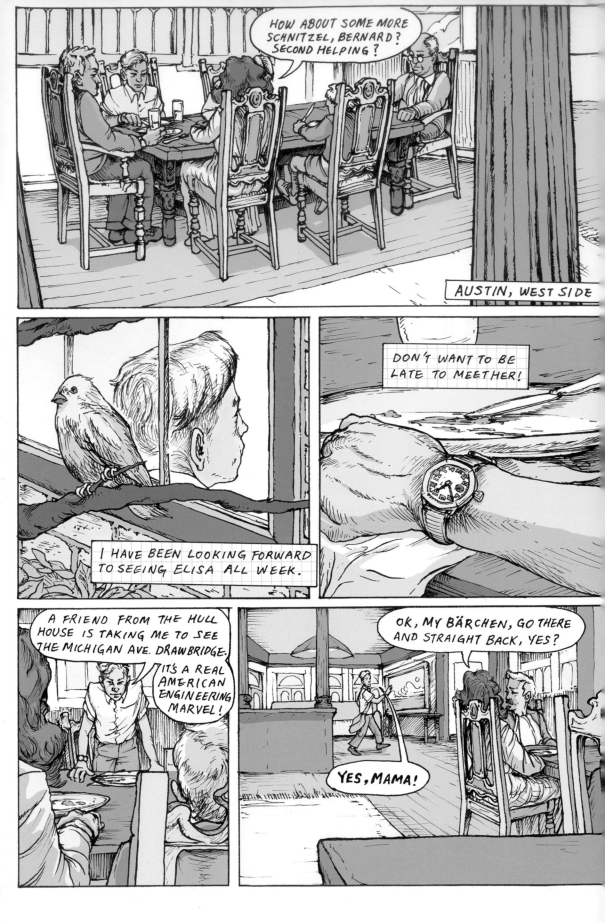

...MUST BE DOWN ON THEIR LUCK.

THIS MUST BE SKID ROW.

UNCLE DIETER TOLD ME ABOUT THIS.

THIS IS THE HEART OF THE MACHINE.

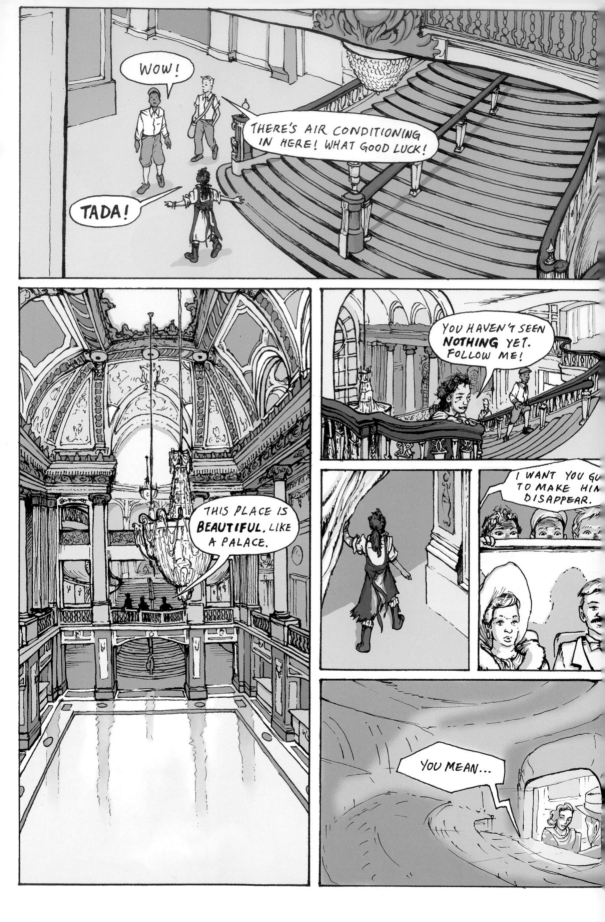

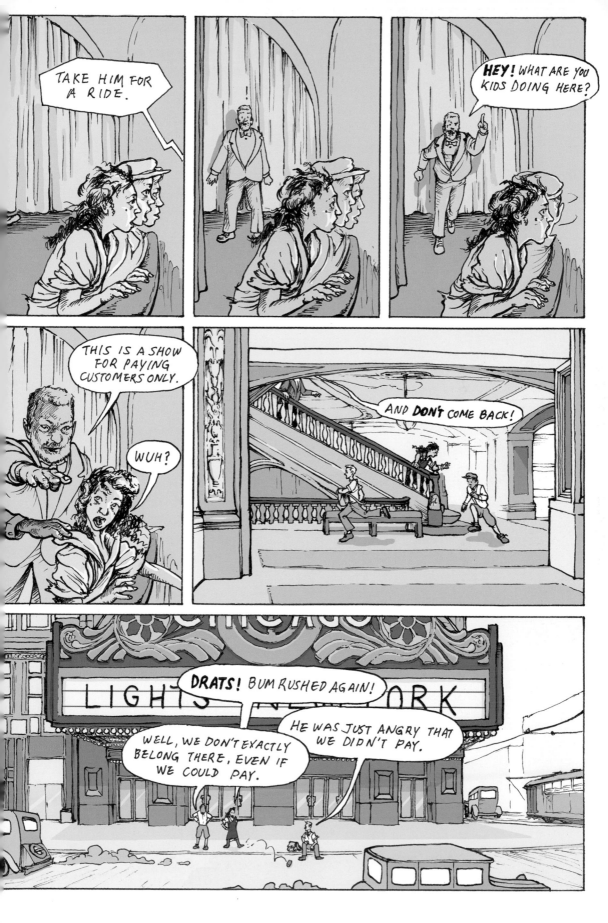

34

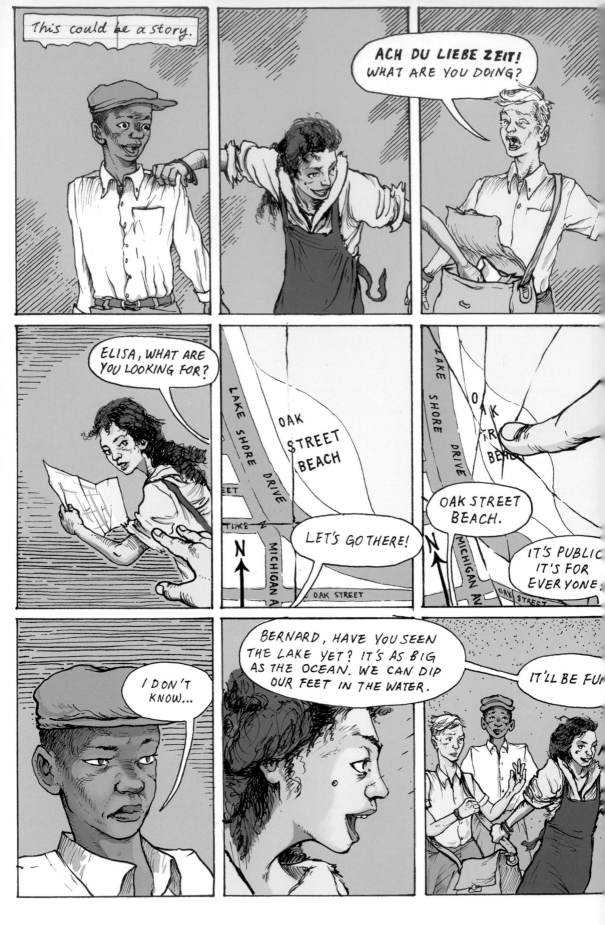

BRIDGING THE CITY
By Reginald Williams

The Michigan Avenue bridge is an icon of Chicago, our city beautiful. As the bridge divides it becomes two leaves pointing toward the sky. In the delicate balance between weight and counterweight, the City sits suspended in its own magnificent engineering. But a city is both its architecture and its people. As citizens we must ask, "How migh[t] we build in ways that unite us? For whom IS this great city of ours?"

DING!

43

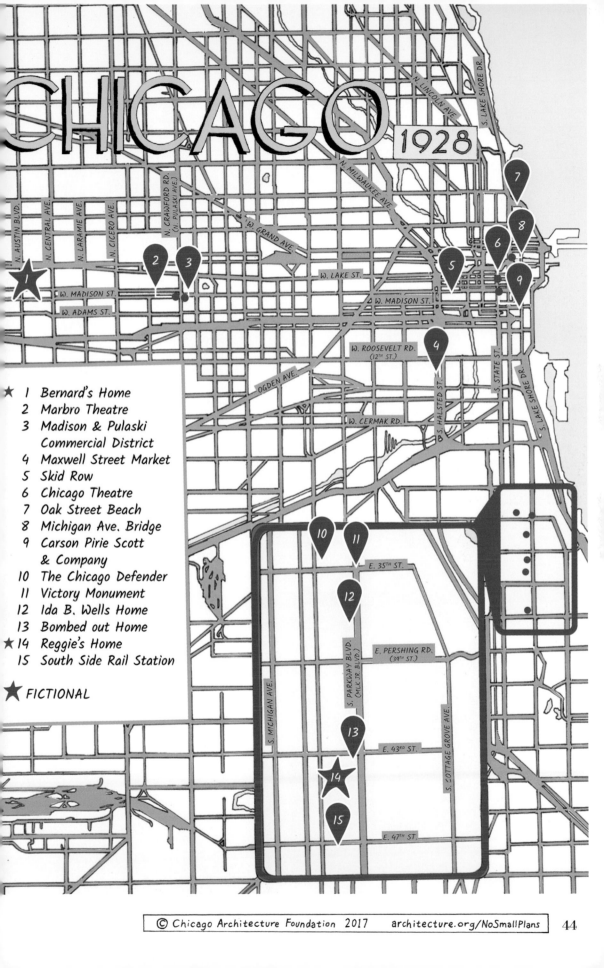

CHICAGO 1928

Map Legend:

★ 1 Bernard's Home
2 Marbro Theatre
3 Madison & Pulaski
   Commercial District
4 Maxwell Street Market
5 Skid Row
6 Chicago Theatre
7 Oak Street Beach
8 Michigan Ave. Bridge
9 Carson Pirie Scott
   & Company
10 The Chicago Defender
11 Victory Monument
12 Ida B. Wells Home
13 Bombed out Home
★ 14 Reggie's Home
15 South Side Rail Station

★ FICTIONAL

Burnham Interlude 1

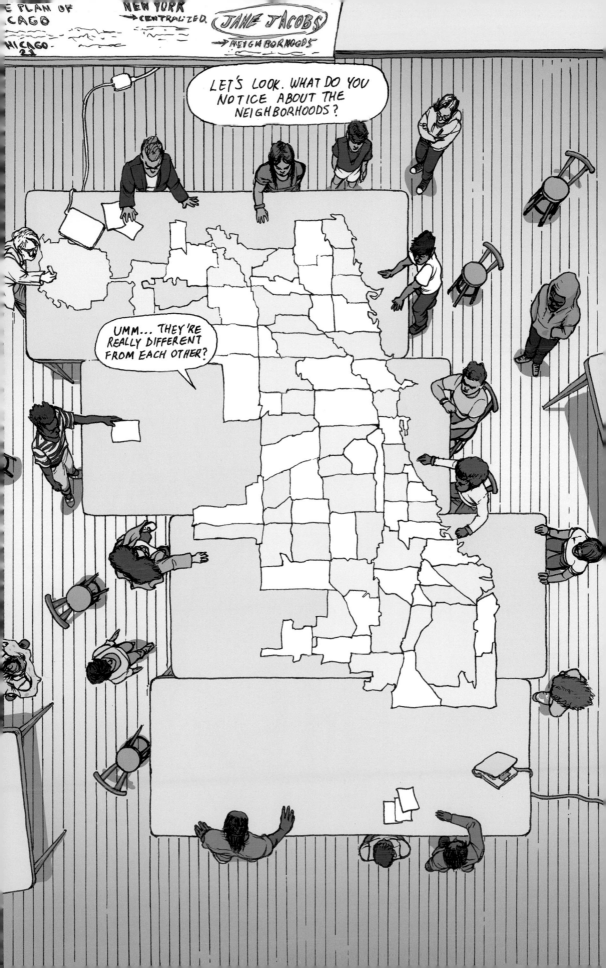

56

72

80

81

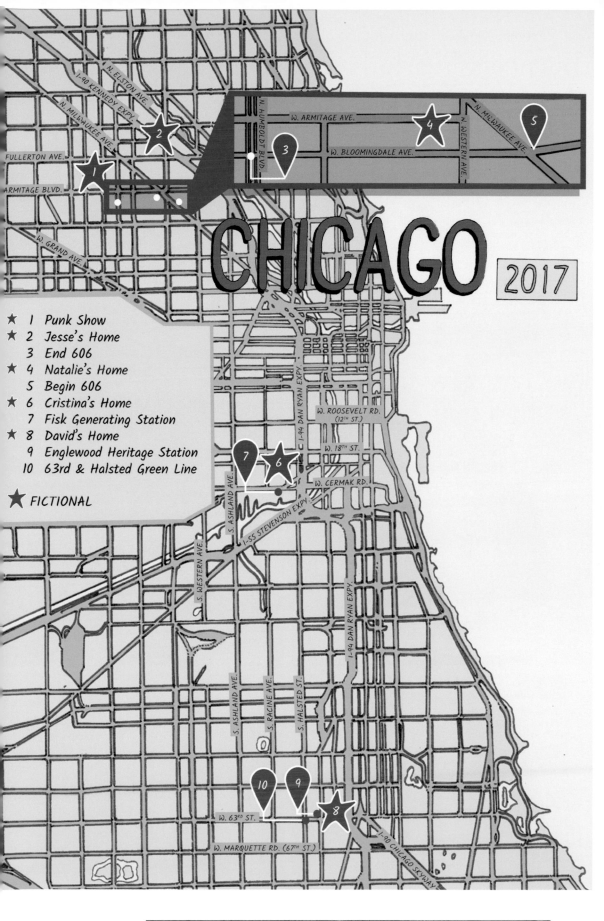

CHICAGO 2017

★ 1 Punk Show
★ 2 Jesse's Home
   3 End 606
★ 4 Natalie's Home
   5 Begin 606
★ 6 Cristina's Home
   7 Fisk Generating Station
★ 8 David's Home
   9 Englewood Heritage Station
  10 63rd & Halsted Green Line

★ FICTIONAL

Burnham Interlude 2

architecture.org/NoSmallPlans

88

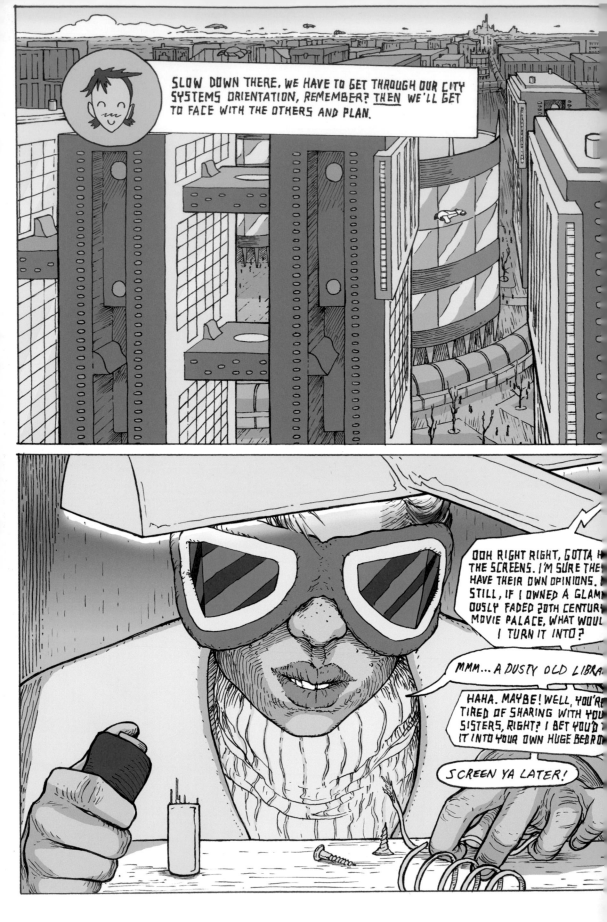

93

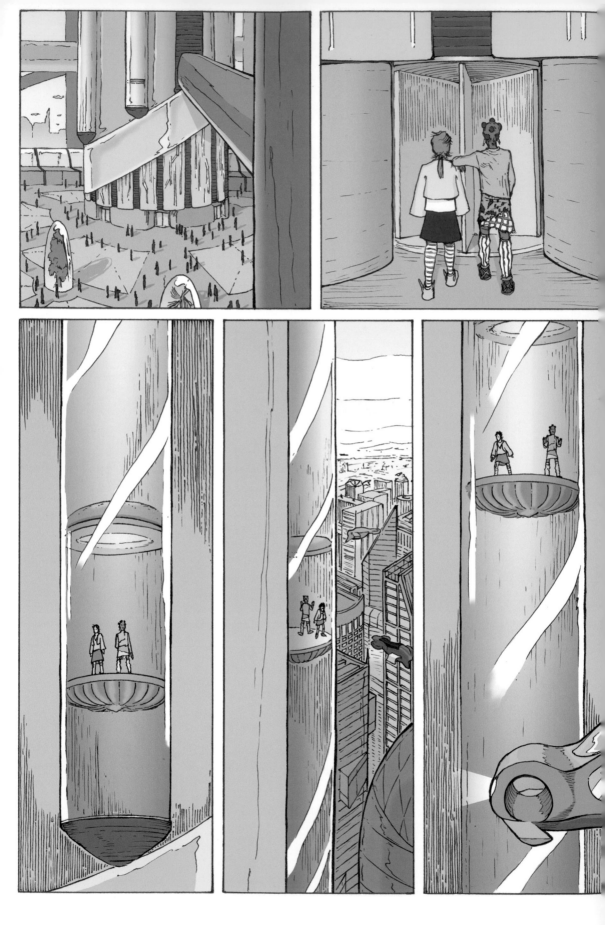

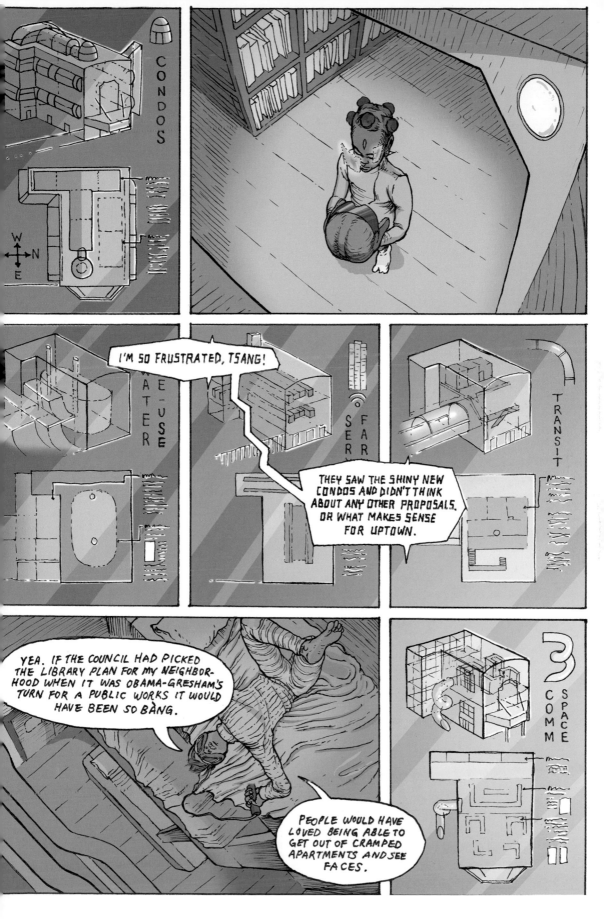

103

104

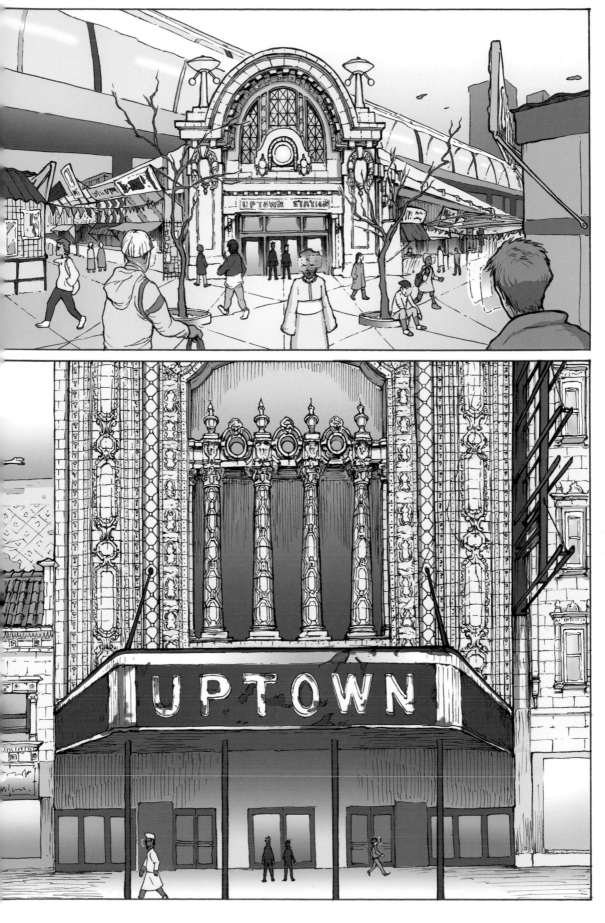

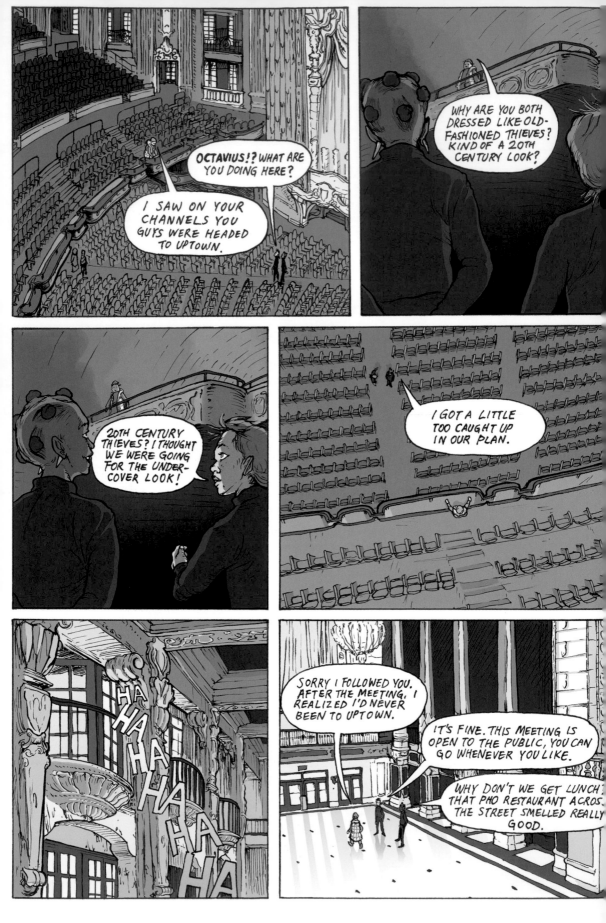

109

110

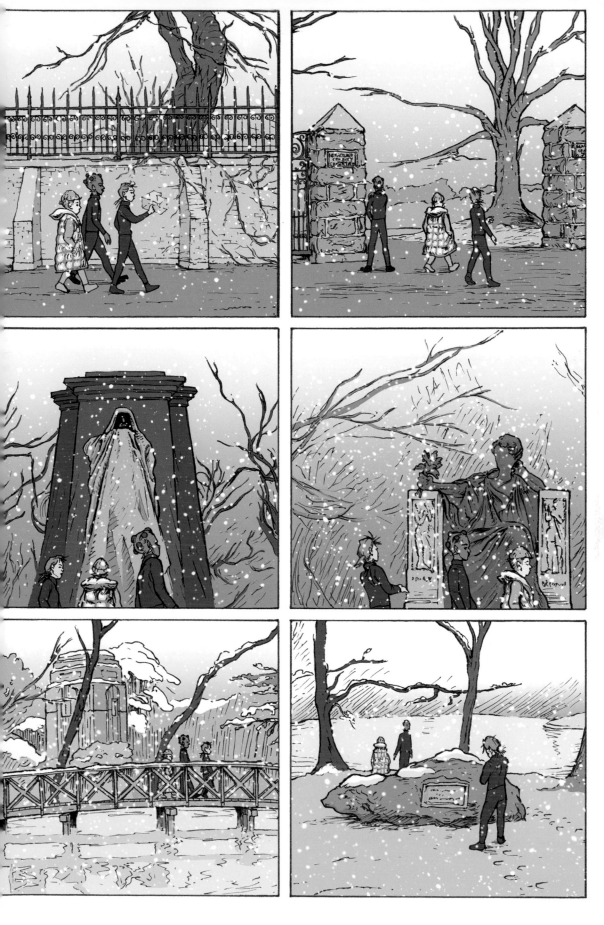

120

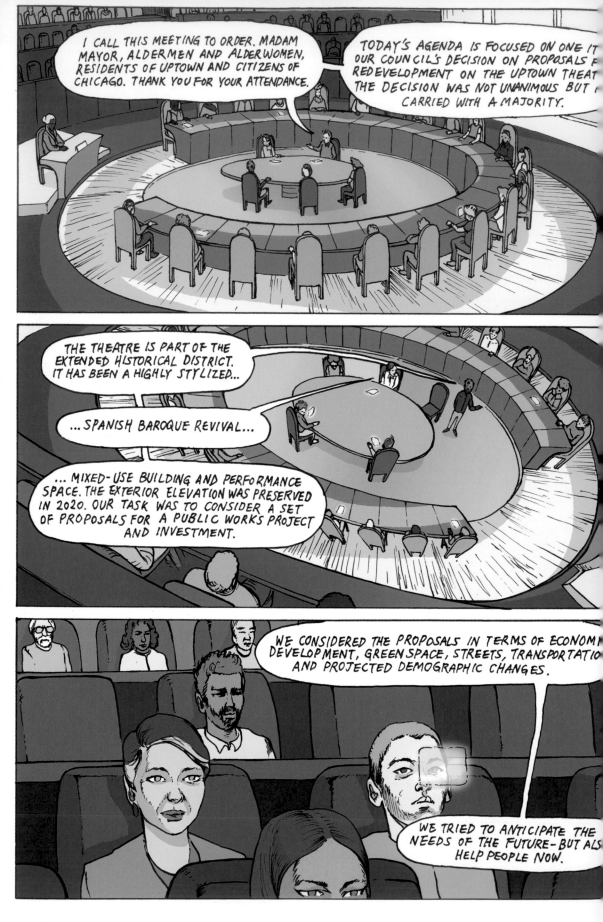

AS THE FUTURE HEADS OF HOUSEHOLDS, IT WAS OUR DUTY TO STEWARD THIS DECISION IN A WAY THAT WOULD BE GOOD FOR THE CITY - AND FOR THE CITIZENS OF UPTOWN.
WE PRESENT TO YOU OUR DECISION. WE LOOK FORWARD TO BREAKING GROUND IN PARTNERSHIP WITH THE INFRASTRUCTURE AND PUBLIC WORKS DEPARTMENT NEXT MONTH...

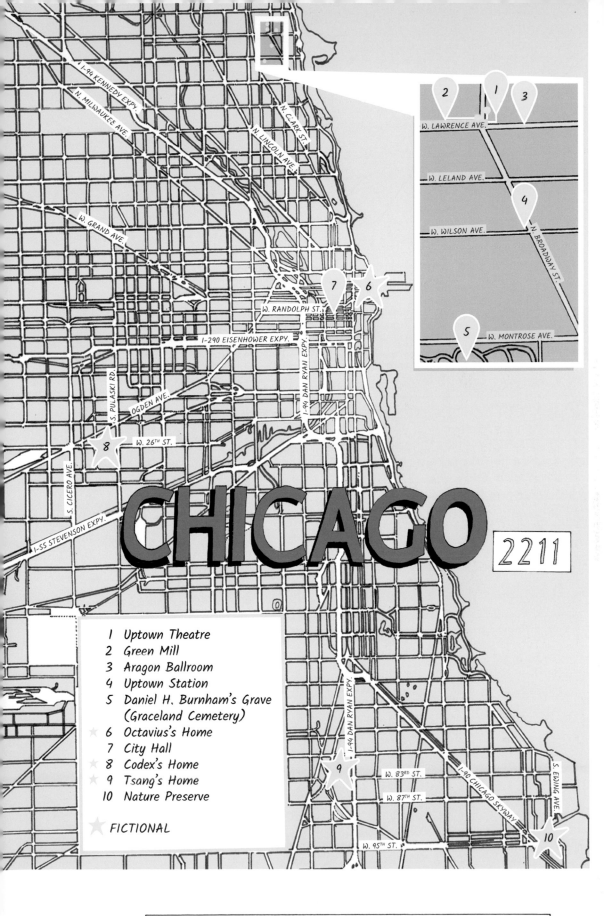

W. LAWRENCE AVE.

W. LELAND AVE.

W. WILSON AVE.

W. MONTROSE AVE.

W. RANDOLPH ST.

I-290 EISENHOWER EXPY.

OGDEN AVE.

W. 26TH ST.

CHICAGO

2211

I-94 KENNEDY EXPY.

N. MILWAUKEE AVE.

N. LINCOLN AVE.

N. CLARK ST.

N. BROADWAY ST.

W. GRAND AVE.

S. PULASKI RD.

S. CICERO AVE.

I-55 STEVENSON EXPY.

I-94 DAN RYAN EXPY.

W. 83RD ST.

W. 87TH ST.

W. 95TH ST.

I-90 CHICAGO SKYWAY

S. EWING AVE.

1 Uptown Theatre
2 Green Mill
3 Aragon Ballroom
4 Uptown Station
5 Daniel H. Burnham's Grave
   (Graceland Cemetery)
6 Octavius's Home
7 City Hall
8 Codex's Home
9 Tsang's Home
10 Nature Preserve

★ FICTIONAL

NOTES

Reader's Guide

No Small Plans follows the adventures of teens in Chicago's past, present and future as they wrestle with designing the city they want, need and deserve. *No Small Plans* takes place in three time periods: 1928, 2017 and 2211. Each chapter ends with a map showing where the story takes place.

If you want to read more about the characters and their neighborhoods, visit the Reader's Toolkit at **architecture.org/NoSmallPlans**. We hope *No Small Plans* inspires you to explore your neighborhood and design the city you want, need and deserve.

Chapter 1: The Past, 1928

In 1928 Chicago, at the height of the construction boom following the 1909 *Plan of Chicago*, Reggie, Elisa and Bernard defy social codes to spend an afternoon together downtown. They run headlong into the contradictions of racial and class discrimination, and they must decide to stand and fight or protest another day, another way.

Reginald (Reggie) Williams is the son of two business owners in Bronzeville. His parents migrated to Chicago's Black Belt from Mississippi in the 1910s to escape the racial violence and discrimination of the South and find new opportunities in the North. They own a diner in the heart of the Black Metropolis known as Bronzeville. Reggie is a paperboy for the *Chicago Defender*. He wants to be a journalist.

Reggie met **Elisa Gallo** at her food stand on Maxwell Street when his parents sent him to the market to buy supplies. Orphaned when she was four, Elisa has been cared for by an elderly woman. Elisa refers to her as 'Mammina.' They live together in a tenement near Taylor Street. She works at the food stand in the Maxwell Street Market and is an active member of the Hull House community, a settlement house established by Jane Addams and Ellen Gates Starr. She helps teach English to new immigrants; this is how she met Bernard.

Bernard Richter is a recent immigrant whose family fled Germany after World War I. They live in a bungalow in Austin, a neighborhood on the city's West Side that attracted many upwardly mobile Germans and Scandinavians. Bernard is fascinated by engineering marvels constructed during the industrial heyday of Chicago in the 1920s. He tells his family he is going to meet his cousin but really he wants to spend time with Elisa. He's disappointed when he sees Reggie because he thought he would be spending the day alone with her.

This chapter raises the question: ***Who is the city for?***

OTHER QUESTIONS TO CONSIDER

- Reggie, Elisa and Bernard see different things as they travel downtown. Based on what they see during their trips, who do you think the city is for?

- Do you agree with how Elisa, Bernard and Reggie each responded to the bullies on the beach? What would you have done if you had been there?

- How do Elisa and Reggie participate in their communities? How do you participate in your community?

- Do you think the three characters will meet up again?

Chapter 2: The Present, 2017

Jesse, David and Cristina realize classroom discussions about zoning, fair housing, gentrification and displacement are real, urgent issues when they discover their friend Natalie is being evicted. Their backgrounds give each of them a unique point of view about neighborhood change. As they work to support Natalie they become involved with Chicago's history of development, organizing and resistance, and they begin to understand that making change takes community.

Cristina Gonzalez is part of an extended Mexican-American family with deep roots in Pilsen. When she was a baby, Cristina's parents were active in the neighborhood's fight to close the nearby coal-fired electric power plant and often took her to rallies. She attends a public arts magnet high school in Logan Square along with David, Jesse and Natalie.

David Green is being raised by his construction-worker father in Englewood. Their home, an 1890s Greystone three-flat apartment building commonly found in the area has been in his family for several generations. David produces music and can usually be found with headphones hanging on his shoulders. To get to high school, David commutes an hour each way on the bus. He met his new friend, Jesse, at school.

Jesse Schoenherr is son of a two-parent middle-class family. He loves photography and carries his camera everywhere. Unlike Natalie, who has lived in Logan Square her whole life, Jesse's family moved to the neighborhood at the start of the school year. Jesse is an enthusiastic newcomer to the area, but he is unfamiliar with its history and culture.

Natalie Guerrero has been raised in the same Logan Square neighborhood apartment where her mother grew up. Natalie is unaware of the fast-rising rents and new construction in Logan Square and Humboldt Park until she learns that her family is being evicted because their apartment building is being sold for redevelopment. When Natalie shares her news with her friends, they help her start to connect her personal experience with the experiences of other people and other communities.

This chapter raises the questions: ***What is the relationship between development and displacement? What does community involvement look like?***

OTHER QUESTIONS TO CONSIDER

- Why do you think it took Natalie so long to share her news with her friends? How do you think you would have responded to this kind of news from your friend?

- What does the photo album at Cristina's house depict? What lessons do Cristina's parents share with the group? How does Natalie respond to the information?

- What does Jesse take photos of at the beginning of the chapter? What about at the end of the chapter? What do you think the photos say about how Jesse is changing?

- What kinds of things does David observe as he walks through his neighborhood? What does he imagine? Have you ever imagined how your neighborhood could be different? What would you change or add? Who would those changes affect?

- Do you agree with the elderly woman gardening who says, "gotta participate." Can you think of ways your neighborhood has changed? Who was affected by the changes?

- What do you think happened when David went into the alderman's office at the end of the chapter?

Chapter 3: The Future, 2211

In the year 2211, Chicago is geographically segregated and virtual reality is the primary bridge for staying connected across neighborhoods. Teens Octavius, Tsang, Codex, Gabriela and Rafael are assigned to the City Planning Council for their Year of Civic Service. They struggle to come together to make decisions that will affect a neighborhood that none of them live in.

Codex Edwards loves the 19th and 20th centuries: she dresses up in styles from 250 years ago, listens to old music, collects historic objects and quotes out-of-date phrases. Codex lives in New Lawndale on the city's West Side. Codex is passionate about the city and is thoughtful about how decisions are made and who will be affected. Codex has been connected with Tsang via a virtual reality channel, but until they were placed onto the same civic assignment, they had never met face-to-face.

Tsang Minato-Qui is an introvert, tech-nerd and data lover. A resident of the Obama-Gresham neighborhood on the city's South Side, she loves new inventions, puzzles, patterns and systems. Tsang has applied to the Illinois Institute of Technology (IIT) for an apprenticeship. When Gabriela and Rafael offer to help her in exchange for her vote on the planning council, she is faced with a serious dilemma.

Gabriela and **Rafael Yao** are cousins. Like Octavius, they live in City Core and are part of the city's upper class. The Yaos are glad to have been placed on the Planning Council and believe it is an opportunity to support their family's business.

Octavius Bacca lives in an elite residential tower in the City Core district in downtown Chicago as part of the city's upper class. His knowledge of other people with different life experiences is limited. Octavius has access to premium accounts for all his technology subscriptions—including teleportation and 3D-printed foodstuffs. His parents often talk to him about making good decisions that will impact his long-range future. Until his experience on the Planning Council with Tsang and Codex, he has not been challenged to think deeply about the impact of his choices.

This chapter raises the questions: ***Who decides? How are decisions made in my city? What's my role and my responsibility?***

OTHER QUESTIONS TO CONSIDER

- What surprises you about 2211? Are there any aspects of the future that seem familiar?

- How does each character make a decision about which proposal to accept? What personal experiences influence their decisions?

- Why do Tsang and Codex decide to go to Uptown? Why motivates Octavius? Does the experience in Uptown change their perspectives at all? Do you think it was a good idea to go to Uptown? Why or why not?

- What does Octavius mean when he says "I was wrong to think I could make a decision from my apartment?" Do you agree with him?

- What are Rafael and Gabriela trying to get Tsang to do? Why? What advice would you give Tsang? If you were in Tsang's position, what would you do?

- Who has power in the group? How do they use their power?

Burnham Interludes

In between each chapter are "interludes" that bring architect and urban planner Daniel Burnham—and the art and science of urban planning—to life.

QUESTIONS TO CONSIDER

- What does Daniel Burnham mean in Interlude Three when he says, "The decisions were not mine alone?"

- In the last frame on the last page, Daniel Burnham challenges readers to "Have at it." What does he mean? What kinds of things would you need to consider if you were going to design a city for "everyone?"

- Do you think the city planners did a good job where you live? What did they do well? What would you add or change to make where you live more "livable for everyone?"

No Small Plans and Meet Your City

No Small Plans was inspired by *Wacker's Manual*, a 1911 textbook that was required reading for all 8th graders in Chicago Public Schools for nearly three decades. *Wacker's Manual* taught young people about the building blocks of the city and the goals of the 1909 *Plan of Chicago*. It also challenged readers to steward the city to greatness through "united civic efforts." Although not fully realized, the 1909 *Plan of Chicago* was one of the country's earliest and most important comprehensive urban plans.

When Chicago Architecture Foundation (CAF) staff shared *Wacker's Manual* with our Teen Fellows, the teens were riveted by the story of Chicago's city plan and the profound responsibility *Wacker's Manual* expected. The Fellows asked, "Why isn't there anything like this for students to read today?" We wondered the same thing.

We spent 2015 talking with dozens of teens, teachers, urban planners and community organizations about the question "What's most worth knowing and experiencing about civic engagement and urban planning?" This exercise helped us think about themes that are important for today's young people. In spring of 2016, we announced a competition for Midwestern artists to propose concepts for a new graphic novel that would address, "Chicago's past, present and future; architecture as a character; youth as change agents; and the city's grit and shine." With help from our Advisory Committee and our Teen Fellows, we selected the winners: Devin Mawdsley, Kayce Bayer, Chris Lin and Deon Reed, an artist collective known as Eyes of the Cat Illustration.

The result is *No Small Plans*, a book that follows the neighborhood adventures of teens in Chicago's past, present and future as they wrestle with designing the city they want, need and deserve. The artwork is inspired by photographs, real places and stories from Chicago. The Burnham Interludes were written, in part, using actual quotes from historic figures. Daniel Burnham believed in the power of big ideas and the title of this book plays with a quote often attributed to him: "Make no little plans; they have no magic to stir men's blood." For the young people in this graphic novel, there is no such thing as a "small" plan.

In 2017, in honor of our 50th anniversary, CAF launched a three-year initiative called Meet Your City designed to address the civic education gap. *No Small Plans* is at the heart of this initiative. Through partnerships with Chicago Public Schools, the Chicago Public Library and other organizations, CAF will give away 30,000 copies of *No Small Plans* for free to Chicago students in grades 6-10. We'll also support teachers and students through trainings and workshops in order to catalyze civic engagement and city stewardship.

About the *No Small Plans* Toolkit

No Small Plans aligns with Chicago, Illinois and national social studies, language arts and civic education standards. The toolkit includes essays from leading urban planners and educators to help teachers think about how to use *No Small Plans* as a jumping off point for fostering civic engagement, action projects and urban planning. The toolkit also includes an annotated reader's guide that follows each chapter page by page; community area information; and links to maps, archival photographs, newspaper articles and community data sources. The reader's guide poses critical questions that explore themes in urban planning and civic engagement such as:

Who is the city for?
How are decisions made in my city?
What is the relationship between neighborhood development and displacement?

How do neighborhoods change over time?
What does participation look like?
What is my role and my responsibility in shaping the future of my community?

No Small Plans is accompanied by a free online toolkit available at **architecture.org/NoSmallPlans**.

Stay Involved with *No Small Plans*

Visit **architecture.org/NoSmallPlans** to help ensure all of Chicago's young people are equipped to design the city they want, need and deserve. The website includes links for:

- *accessing the full reader's guide*
- *signing up for student field trips or teacher workshops*
- *buying copies of* No Small Plans
- *making a donation to support the Meet Your City initiative*
- *if you are a Chicago teacher, you can request to be put on a wait-list for free copies for your students*

Every copy of *No Small Plans* sold enables CAF to give a copy away for free. Bulk and educator rates are available by emailing **groupsales@architecture.org**.

About the Authors

Gabrielle Lyon

Born in New Mexico and raised in New York and New Jersey, Gabrielle (Gabe) Lyon has spent most of her life fighting for better educational opportunities for Chicago's youth. In 1994 Gabe served as a fellow at the Southern Poverty Law Center's Teaching Tolerance magazine in Alabama. In 1996 she moved back to Chicago to work with the Small Schools Workshop at the University of Illinois at Chicago. In 1999 she founded Project Exploration, a nonprofit organization dedicated to changing the face of science for underserved minority youth and girls. As the vice president of education and experience at CAF, Gabe is responsible for leading the organization's thinking on how to best enable youth, educators, mentors and families to explore the built environment and design thinking.

Gabe received a Chicago Community Trust Leadership Award in 2009 and, in 2011, *Chicago* magazine named her a "Chicagoan of the Year." Gabe studied medieval history and the history of anthropology at the University of Chicago and got her doctorate in education at the University of Illinois at Chicago. Gabe is the mom of two awesome kids, Ava and Arlo, discovered a dinosaur named *Deltadromeus*, and may have missed her calling as an urban planner. *No Small Plans* is her first (but not last) graphic novel project.

Devin Mawdsley

Devin is a global child of the 1990s, raised in multiple countries, native to none, but is proud to finally make his home in Chicago. Devin has worked for the past 10 years as an educator in various capacities. This began with an interest in language education; having taught both English and Chinese, Devin led student expeditions and taught digital photography through National Geographic in China, served as an associate instructor of fundamental drawing at Indiana University, developed original curricula and taught at the Evanston Art Center.

For the past six years Devin has tied his stake to the growth and success of his students at the Chicago High School for the Arts, developing and teaching the fundamental drawing component of ChiArts' pre-professional visual arts conservatory. He recently co-taught an 8th grade social studies course through CAPE, entitled Photography and the New Civil Rights.

In addition to his experience as an educator, Devin also maintains a diverse studio practice. His current work consists primarily of developing and illustrating graphic novels, as well as an ongoing abstract painting/collage practice. He recently founded the Eyes of the Cat Illustration studio. Devin hopes to use Eyes of the Cat as a vehicle to harness the power of compelling narrative and help raise collective consciousness in troubled times, telling stories by and for the people. **devinmawdsley.com eyesofthecatillustration.com**

Kayce Bayer

Kayce is an artist, educator and mom living in Logan Square since 2005. Originally from North Florida, Kayce moved to Memphis, Tennessee to complete her MFA from the Memphis College of Art, and finally made her way to the big city of Chicago. Kayce's art practice is varied—working through drawing, small objects, video, installation and performance—and more recently includes organizing collaborative creative events that explore personal histories, community and informal art experiences. Her biggest project to date combined many of her creative interests to revisit the vaudevillian form and learn Chicago neighborhood history. "The Great Fire: A Traveling Truck Show" toured Chicago neighborhoods with a moving truck as a pop-up stage, engaging audiences with local history, storytelling, music, art performance and magic. Kayce has over 15 years experience as an arts and design educator working with students of all ages. She is proud and honored to currently spend her days with the amazing young people at the Chicago High School for the Arts. As a teacher, collaborative event organizer and stuff-maker, Kayce sees art as a place to inspire wonder, curiosity and inquiry. She hopes this project will do just that. With a new focus on the intersection of visual art and critical literacy, she is feeling out her next creative moves. Stay tuned. **kaycebayer.com**

Chris Lin

A transplant to Chicago via Taiwan and Canada, Chris Lin is an arts educator and studio artist working in a variety of areas including video, performance, installation, illustration, music and writing. Chris received his MFA in fiber and material studies from the School of the Art Institute of Chicago in 2008. His studio practice explores subjects of reenactment and documentary, seeking to both perpetuate and debunk personal narrative and mythology. He has exhibited extensively in the U.S. and Canada, including group exhibitions in Contemporary Art Workshop, Southside Hub of Production, Chicago Art Department, Eel Space and The Franklin in Chicago; Verge Art Fair in New York; Atlantic Center for the Arts in New Smyrna Beach, FL; and Fifty Fifty Arts Collective, Deluge Contemporary and The Ministry of Casual Living in Victoria, BC, Canada. He currently teaches sequential art and visual communications at the Chicago High School for the Arts where he has, over five years, developed and refined curriculum which aims to cultivate socially-conscious, emotionally-empathetic and media-savvy values. **cardboardish.com**

Deon Reed

Deon is a Chicago-born native, residing in Englewood, who works in multiple disciplines in the arts due to family investment and training from facilities such as Marwen, Palette & Chisel and the Chicago High School for the Arts. He's a product of the Chicago Public Schools system, has a great understanding of said system, and has grown alongside CPS's improvements and setbacks over the years at many public schools on the South Side. At ChiArts, he took art classes in a wide range of practices such as graphic design and sculpture as well as taught himself 3D modeling and still to this day, as an alumnus, uses that information to grow and expand in Chicago's vivid art scene. Since graduating, he's collaborated with multiple artists around the city such as Jeremiah Spofford, a mixed media sculptor based at the Hyde Park Art Center, and Josh Garber, a metal sculptor who is based at Fire Arts Center of Chicago on the North Side. Deon is now focused on taking his artistic abilities to the next level both commercially and conceptually. He's in the process of starting a screen printing business and creating and collaborating with other local artists on projects ranging from audio engineering to film. **deonreed.com**

Acknowledgments

At the Chicago Architecture Foundation (CAF) we believe that Chicago is the best place to inspire the public to build a better future. Since 1966, CAF has inspired people to discover why design matters through tours, exhibitions and programs that illustrate how architecture can improve lives. *No Small Plans* is CAF's gift to Chicago in thanks for all the city has given to us over our first 50 years.

In 2015, we began using a 1911 textbook, *Wacker's Manual*, to teach urban planning to our Teen Academy. Conceived by the Commercial Club to promote the 1909 *Plan of Chicago*, *Wacker's Manual* was required reading for all 8th graders in Chicago Public Schools. The book, for which Chicago owes the Commercial Club a debt of gratitude, sought to "make the child feel that in him [or her] rests the responsibility of assisting Chicago to attain her future greatness." A generation of Chicagoans, including Mayor Richard J. Daley, learned about city building from *Wacker's Manual*. We believe *No Small Plans* will do the same for a new generation of Chicagoans.

I am grateful to the authors and illustrators of the book: Gabrielle Lyon, CAF's vice president of education and experience; and Eyes of the Cat Illustration: Devin Mawdsley, Kayce Bayer, Chris Lin and Deon Reed.

A special thanks to the many CAF staff members who contributed to *No Small Plans*, including Jen Masengarb, director of interpretation and research, and our graphic designers, Allison Leake and Alyssa Sander.

Our friends at Chicago Public Schools and Chicago Public Library will help get *No Small Plans* into the hands of 30,000 Chicago students in grades 6–10 over the next three years. Reaching so many young Chicagoans is made possible by the generous support of the American Planning Association, Microsoft, the Tawani Foundation, CAF's many supporters at the 2017 CAF Annual Gala and more than 1,250 Kickstarter backers.

We hope all our readers will take on the challenge of making no small plans.

**Lynn J. Osmond, Hon AIA, CAE, President & CEO,
Chicago Architecture Foundation**

Thank You to Our Supporters

The first print run of *No Small Plans* was made possible thanks to a Kickstarter campaign run March 27–April 30, 2017 and support from the CAF Annual Gala on April 6, 2017. An asterisk (*) indicates Gala 2017 supporters.

DANIEL BURNHAM ($10,000)

PAUL LARSON

ELLA FLAGG YOUNG ($5,000)

 SUSAN AND
BOB WISLOW*

JULES GUERIN

Karen and
Jay Case*

Digital Youth
Network

In Memory of
Daniel R. Schuh

WALTER D. MOODY

Mary and Joseph Burns*

Christina and
Bob Chodos*

Amy Eshleman

Victoria Herget and
Robert Parsons*

Brian Lee, SOM*

Mercury Skyline Yacht
Charters Inc.*

Erica C. Meyer
in memory of
Lee F. Meyer*

Jill and Lee Pollock*

Kim and Steve Theiss*

EDWARD BENNETT

Donald Anderson
and Anisha Amin

Bleak Beauty

Thomas E Brean*

Michael Forbes

Andrew Giraldi, AICP

Melanie Grune

Amber Hopp-
Schmidt

Julie Jacobson

John Elder Lloyd

Emma and Hanque
Macari

G. Masengarb

Valerie Mawdsley

Joann and Kevin
Murphy

Jim Parsons*

Barbara Radner

April and Bob Rinder

Alberto G. Ruocco

Daniel Shurz and
Katharine Lee

Laurie A Stearn

Adrianne Steichen

Michael Tobin

Steven Vance,
Chicago Cityscape

Tom Wilseck

ACROTERION

Ann Thompson, AIA*
Arlen Productions*
Susan and David Eblen*
Sandra and Jack Guthman*
Nila Leiserowitz
Catherine A. Osika*
Mark Prindiville*
Jeffrey M. Goodenbour
Mario Imbarrato*
Beverley Sibblies*
Soren FutureArchitect Shirtcliff
Chip Ferguson
Lynn Osmond and Christopher Multhauf*
Arber Asanoski
Jesse Banwart
David Bartolai*
Luis Bettencourt
Jean Boland
Jeffrey Brown
Marshall Brown*
Philip Cable
Stacey and Lowell Cantor
Polly Carpenter FAIA
MH Chappetto

Joe Cliggott
Menachem Cohen
Thomas M. Colwell
Ian Coppell
Alex Czurylo
Diana
Geralyn Donovan
Jean Dufresne
Josh Ellis
Bridget Fallon
Douglas Farr
Scott Fenwick & Sarah Barr
Catherine L. Fey
Todd Fitz
Josh B. Fox
Kevin Freed
Joe Germuska
Mitch Glass
Mike Gold
Diana Gonzales
James J. Grogan
Paul Hagman—RBF CoLab Architecture
Christopher Hale*
Denise Hall*
Bethann Hester
Joshua Hill
Charles Hogh
Vicki Hsu

Renee L Huebner
Lori Hypes
Edson Burton, Jr*
Kurt Karnatz
John Kelley
Jenny Lau
Oren Levin
Paul and Victoria Liebenson*
Jason Lindquist
Annclaire Livoti
Aaron M. Lopata
Judy and Tom Lubin
J.S. Majer
Christopolis Tiberius Markus
Jen Masengarb
Kimberly Mayhall
Robert McCoy
Keith McCready
Patrick Miner
Mary Monroy-Spampinato
Dr. and Mrs. Robert G. Morrison, Jr.
Jessi Moths
Cynthia Muller
Jenni Groot Mushynski
Andrew E Mushynski

Michael J Lee Niehaus
Lynne Considine Nieman*
Jenny Niemann*
Kurt Olson + Melissa Toops
Deborah Orr
Michelle Panovich*
Julio Paz and Veronica Reyes
Ellen Peterson
Britton Picciolini
John Pintozzi
Wendy Kramer Posner
Quinn Raymond
Sendhil Revuluri
anne c roberts
The Roseberry Family
Gwen Rousseu
Vicky Sanchez & Juan Perez
Chiara Santini*
John and Cynthia Savage
Paula & Jim Schriner
Boaz Shalit
Stephanie Sheridan

Gillian Siegel and Steven Gillman
Wendy Siegel
Vicki S
Joe Sislow
Oezlem & Cihan Soeguet
Laura Speck
Cyndie Spudic
Kent Steffen
Julie Swislow
Jill Tanz
Tiffany
Nelson Trautman
Christy Uchida
Margi Ungrodt & Curt Renner
Stelios Valavanis
Suzanne Vestuto
Lisa Voigt and John Dodson
Drew Weissman
Cassidy Williams & Joseph Song
Suzanne McSherry Wimsatt
Kate Wolf
Eric Wolff
Yagcier-Rodriguez Family
Elaine Yoo
Margo Yoon
Fotios Zemenides

ARCH

Joy Abella
Ivy Ellen Abid
Torsten Adair
Kerstin Grune Adams
Jesse Agnew
Benjamin Aldred
Amieling
Kristen M. Andersen
Jon and Heather Armbruster
Agnès Artemel
Paul F. Aubin
Elizabeth Auman*
Ioana Balas
Joanna B

Amy B. Bashiti
Michael Battin
graham beer
Josh Bergman
Jennifer Berk
Jake Berlin
Helene Berlin
barrett
Katherine and Sam Best
Beth
Bitsy
Boeman Design
Daniel Borchelt, Somerville, MA
Michiel Born
Mo & Jer Bot

Brian Boyer
Kathryn Bradley
Glen Brixey
Caroline Brown
Anja Bruehling
Jane R. Buckwalter*
William Burg
Bree
Joy Calaoagan
Vanessa Jasmine Campisi
Cat Caracci
Vanessa Casciano*
Kelly Casey
Anthony Cefali

Nicol Chervenak*
Natasha R. Chisdes
Erica J Christianson
Jeana Clark
James Clary
Jason Crase
Lafayette Cruise
Charles Czerkawski*
Andrew Daglas
Samantha J. Dahlstrom
Stephanie De Bonth
Ian Dees
Anita DeMeo

Cheryl Devall
Shokoufeh Dianat
John Donmoyer
Lyla Dove
Ruth Droescher
Rashid Durham
Anika
Andy Eng
Damian Ennis
In Honor of Jeffrey & Lawrence Evans
Family Friendly Oakland
Kelly Fitzgerald
Marie and Brian Fitzpatrick

Jeff Fluhr
Erica Foster
Nicholas J Frank
Louisa Galassini
James F Garner
Patricia Garza
Laura Gawlinski
Gensler Chicago Employees
Fuzzy & Erica Gerdes
Allie Gerlach
jason gessner
Marco Giordani
Matt Godbolt
Max Goldstein
Pat Gonzales

*Denotes Gala 2017 supporter

ARCH continued

James Gorski
Bill & Jeanne Goulding
Stanley Greenberg
Brad and Ellen Griffin-Stolbach
Sandy M Guettler
Kay Hancox
Alaina J. Harkness
Tim TheWizard Harris
Dr. Jason Harshman
Matt Hatter
Troy Henikoff
Cecilia Herdegen
Paul & Karen Herkes
Nick Hillard
Judith Holtz
Alexis Hope
MRHorhager
Cathy Hroma
Mark J. Hughes
Nausheen Husain
Kristin Hyle
Joan Jablonski
Dale Jacobs
George Jacobsen
Paulette Jacobsmeier

Kristina Maldre Jarosik
R. Ann Jones
Kurt Kemmerer
Ryan Kennedy
Pieter Kers
Helen J Kessler
Dan Kidd
Yoonjeong (Yooni) Kim
James Kleffner
Zak Klehr
STEVE KNABL
Brandy Koch
David Kolodzieczyk
Larissa D. Kosits
Erin & Abe Kruger
Siegfried Kuhlbrodt
Becky Larson
Greg Lavine
Nathan A Leahigh
Bridget Lesniak*
Mr. Conor Libit
Lingelbach Family
Darren Lipman
Heidi S. Lubin
Ava Lyon-Sereno
Arlo Lyon-Sereno
Elsa & Ozzy Lyon
Megan Mackinson
Krissy Mayes

Benjamin McCloskey
Evelyn and Mike McGowan
Sachin Mehta
Stephen Michael Fountain
K. Milam-Brooks
Anna Millham
William Miskovetz
Deborah Mitchell
Michelle Mondro
Elizabeth Monkus & Alessandro X Cuéllar
Sarah Morton Taggart
Alice Munro
Nara Nayar
Jason & Erin Neises
Betty, Greg Nelson
Margaret Newman
Thomas Niederberger
Michael Niosi
Ellen Oberhart
Oscar Newman
Jonathan Oh
Abbey L Oklak
Uri Pachter and Hollen Reischer
Nina Elliot Parker

Pasha
Paula Paul
Lorna Peterson
Barrington [Bear] Pope
Scott and Laurel Preece
Sharon Scott Priest
Edge Quintanilla
Rebekah
Steven James Redmond
Terra L. Reed
David Reifman
Karina Ricks
The Rife Family
Alex Rixey
Gertjan Rohaan
Nik Rokop
Kieron Roost
Adam Rosa
Mitch Rosenfeld
Elory Rozner
Betsy Rubin
Tushar Samant
Laura Samson
VICTOR SAVA
Bob Schaefer
Robert Schaffer
Heidi Schallberg
Vincent J. Schuster
Josephine and Eleanor Seid

Joseph Seliga
Katerina Sergatskova
Ashley Sinclair and Corey Rudolph
town slade
Professor Peter E. Smirniotopoulos
Justin T. Smith
Joyce Ann Smith
Paul Smith
LaSean Smith
Joshua Snyder
Jeffrey Sriver
Drew Stanecki
Alexandra Steveson
Jason P. Stonchus
Kevin Sullivan AIA
Dave Tan
Tara
S Taradash
Damon G. Taylor
Ashley Telman
Derrick Teo
Amber & Braydon Thompson
Morgan Thompson
John Tielsch
William Tippens*
John Tolva

Tommy Travers
Grace Isang
Cam and Ed Twohey
Wesley Urschel
Lauren Van Damme
Jim & Barb Vanderveen
Atul Varma
Crystal and Jeffrey Vaughn
Christopher Veit
Denise Voskuil-Marre
Catherine Vrdolyak
Catherine Warner
Marsha Warren
Michael A. Welch, Jr.
Matt & Kate Westerlund
@MisterWhitaker
Robert W White
Renee Dake Wilson
Joseph & Lavonne Wukas
Jenn Yoo
Ryan Young
Lisa Youngberg
Zetetics
Dimitrios Zoulis

TRUSS

Mark & Marcie Achler
Taylor Adams
Ateet Adhikari
Charles Adler
Steph Adrales
Sunil Agnani
PAOLA AGUIRRE SERRANO
Benjamin Akinbola
Dave Alden
Courtney Alexander
Andrew Alexis
Kareeshma Ali
danny alvarez
Lee E Anderson
Cecil Apostol
aradhna
Bob Armbruster
Carolyn Aronson
Ashlee
Ali Attari
Sarah Avampato
Paul Axel
elaine bachman
Jessica Bader
Susan J. Bandes
Anthony Bandy-Zalatoris, AIA

Christopher J. Banser
David W Bapst
Tom Barnas Jr.
Brittany Barnes
Briauna Barrera
Andrew Barrett-Weiss
Judith Bartosz
Arielle Basich
brian bauman
Dave Baxter
Vince Bayless
Andy Beck
Teri Behm
Erin Bell
Kathryne Benesh
James Benton Radson
Esther Bergdahl
Stephanie Bergren
Jerice Bergstrom
Kelsey Berry
Bennett Berson
Bertetto Family
Rev. Jim Best
Jim Bethune
The Bidani-Dolik Family

Elizabeth Birnbaum
Black Lives Matter
Isabella Blasi
Mitchell Bobman
Sylvia Bochner
Bill Boehmer
Chris Borden
Dana Boutin
Jordan Bouvier
Margaret Perry Bradley
Marie Z. Branch
Erik Brandel-Tanis
brandon
Ellen Braverman
Noah Brick
David Brittain
Trowby Brockman
Paul and Angelee Brockmeyer
Clifford L Brown P.E.
Mary Jo Brown
Clara Brubaker
Andrea Bruckner
Dane Buchholz
Shaun Buckley, Redding, CA

Building Brown Workshop
Building Up Chicago
Ann Bunger
Ms. Burke
Eric Burkman
Gideon Burnett
Rebecca Burns
Marco Buscaglia
Whitney Bush
M. Busscher
Brenna K Bychowski
Ann Cremin Byrne
Rachel Calderon Navarro
Jeffrey C Campbell
Cynthia Campo
Whitney Capps
Joseph Caramagno
Courtney Carreras
Rob Cassidy
Noel Luis Castellanos
Quinn Quihui Castro
Charlie Catlett
Ali Cedroni
Louis Chabardes

Frank J Chambers Jr
Corey Chan
Justin K Chen
Lucy Chen
Jinghui Cheng
Alexander Chin
Sarah Christofersen
Wilder Atlas Chua
Payton Chung
Vincent, Sarah, and Doris Chung
The Ciok Family
Craig Claeys
Alexander Claman
Ben Clark
Clark/Mitchell Family ACL
Joshua Cohen
Rachel Cole
Sydni Cole
Alvin J. Colón
Columbus Underground.com
Odile Compagnon
Tony Contento
Kijana Core
Alice Eleni Costas
Sarah Coulter
Jane Coutre

Ben Cowan
Susanna Craib-Cox
Valerie Craig
Andrea Crain
Nathan Crawford
Cryptowolf
Brian Cudiamat
Sam Kirk & Jennifer Cunningham
Cecily Cunz
Emma Cuciurean-Zapan
Dane
Norma DaRosa
Rebekah Dasari
Natalia Dattilo
Mike Davis
Rebecca Davis
Alex Day
Michael D'Costa
Barbara A. Deardorff
Scott DeGan
Sabrina Degas Pont
Amanda DeGrace
Shannon Delaney
L.Dempsey
Thomas A. Dennis
David Dewane

Giancarlo Di Lonardo
Shaska Dice
Reid Dickman
Benjamin Dickow and Family
Dean Diedrich
Nick Disabato
David W Dittmann
Brendan Doms
Rachel Donofrie
Eileen C. Donovan
Pedro Doria
Sarah Dougher
Brianne Downing
Kathryn Doyle
Stephanie Drago
Dave and Nancy Dribin
Barton Dring
Jon M. Dugan
Aaron L Dunlap
Bruce Dunn
Tom Dyke
Scott Eagleston
PS Ecker
John Edwards
Spencer Edwards
Terry Eisele

Kevin Eisenmann
Tom Elmer
Chris Emery & Teresa Autery
Linda S Englund
Nora Engonopoulos
tiana epps-johnson
Debra Epstein
C. Erbguth
August C Ftsch Jr.
Sonya Evanisko
A & D Evans
Bonnie Fan
Ryan Fant
David Faust
Rudy Faust
Nicole Ferentz
Lance S Ferges
Catherine S. Fillmore
Ann Hilton Fisher
Molly FitzHarris
The Foley Family
Tom Foltyn
Brian Foo
Adam Ford and Jason Bohner
Matt Ford

TRUSS continued

Theresa Ford-Wells
Veronica Foster
Mike Fourcher
Casey Franklin
Natalie Frederick
Jason Freeman
Melanie A. Freimuth
Aleksandra Furman
Patti Jules Fylling
Gary Gaines
Luke Galambos
Chris Gansen
Vicki L. Garza
Pall Gasp-Hardtravelinghero
Lesley Gasparetti
Jeremiah Geiman
Dr. Liz Gerber
Jill Gerber
Kristina Gerlach
Lina S. Germann
John Gianniny
G. Gianos
Zora Gilbert
Sarah R. Glaser
Federico Gomez
Greg Gonzalez
Jackie Gonzalez
Jacob B. Gonzalez
beth gorr
Shelby Goss
Janelle Grace
Jacob J. Graham
Lindsay M Graham
The Grant Family
Max Graziano
Karen Green
Sarah Greenberg
Ryan Griffis
DiDi Grimm
Scott Grimm-Lyon
Melissa Anne Guilbeau
Erica Gunderson
Jess Haley & Andy Allard
Ryan Hamlett
Mark Hammergren
Jane Hanna
David Hardnett
Jessica Goldbogen Harlan
Christian Harrison
Zaid Hassan
Matthew Hatfield
ERIK HAUGSNES
Julia Hawkinson
Christopher Hayner
Brad Heap
heather
Jennifer Henaghan
Dan and Candace Hennessey
Allison Hennie
Matthew Ross Irwin Henricks
John Hergenroeder
Graham Robert Herman
Guy Hermann
Katie Herskovitz
Dr. Diane Hickey-Davis

Brantley Hightower
Aaron & Jenelle Hill
Shannon Hill
Joe Hilliard
Erica T. Hines
Vivian Ho
Randall Hoekstra
AJ Hoff
Erica Holthausen
Anne Holub
Dan Hooker
Jeffrey A Hopkins
Norene Hough
Jessica Lyn Howard
Andrew Huff
michael hurley
Rory Hyde
PJ Hyett
Ruby Hypes
Carolyn Isaacson
Micah T.J. Jackson
Benjamin Moses Jacobi
loretta jacobs
Evan & Shama Jacover
Anne Marie Janeway
Lisa Jastram
Noah Temaner Jenkins
Noah Jeppson
Jeremy
Donna E Jesser
Jessica
Ron Jirsa
Doneliza Joaquin
Anders Johnson
Austin R. Johnson
Denise Johnson
Jessica Johnson
J Lave Johnston
Jana & Lee Joramo
Arthur S Jordan Jr
Grace Jordan
JOSEPH
Jeff Judge
Sam Julian
Rachel L. Juris
Rachel K.
Ben Kaczmarski
Tim Kain
Paige Kaliski
Joan Kallas
Josh Kalov
Miles Kampf-Lassin
Dr. Judith Kaplan-Weinger
Cynthia Davis Karabush
Craig Karas
Edward T Karzes
Sarah Katz
KCGriebenow
Stephanie Kee
Peg Keiner
John Kelly
Megan Kelly
Stephanie Kestelman

Sharon Pinto Khurana
Kiki
Stephen & Rachel Killion
Jae Won Kim
Brooke Kingsley
Molly Kinsella*
Rick Kintigh
Peter Kirschmann
Jennifer Kitson
Meredith Klekotka
Harry Klinkhamer
Craig Koester
Tai Kojro-Badziak, roomTEN design
Kathy Konieczny
Karin Konz
Elizabeth Koprucki
Cal Kotz
Cristina Kovacs
Holly Krejci
Nate Krempel
Joan M. Kripke
P. Kruza
S. J. Kuhn
Ramya Kumaran
Hans Kumler
Anneli Kunze
Patrick La Riviere
Samuel S Lacy
Jessie LaFree
Peggy Lami
The Landman/Feigelson Family
Alexandra Lange
Benjamin H. Lang
Eric Lange
LaRonika Thomas
Scott Larson
Jessica Marcella Lau
Patrick Lau
Matt Lauterbach
Emeric Laverne
B. Le
Katina Leaks
Andrew M Leasure
Edgar Leon
Patrick J. Leonard
Felicia Less
Cinda K. Lester, 12/12 Architects & Planners
Matt Leung
J David Lewis
Paul Lillehaugen
Sam Lima
Eric H. Limbach
Jon Lincoln
Meghan M. Linehan
Sara Lippitt
Benjamin Lipsman
Kim Lisagor Bisheff
Katherine Loftus
Andrew Lohmann
Benny "Boom-Boom" Lonarek
Michelle London
M. David Lopez
Rebecca Lopez
Tyler Lorenzen

Amina and Felix Lowe
Emerson Lowrance
Kimberly Lucas
Stephanie Lucas
Daphne Lundi
Terrence F Lynam
Joseph Lynn
rob lyon
Laura Machala
Sam Maddock
Tim and Donna Madel
Aaron Maertins
Janice Mann
Jeff Marcella
Tony and Kate Marengo
Ms. Amanda K. Margis
Janine Marino
Meaghan Markiewicz
Tiernan Martin
Sonja Marziano
The Ali Pali Massif
Andrew Mathias
J. Michael Matkin
Lisa Mayse-Lillig
Jeff McCarter
Monica McClure
Anne D. McCullough
Matthew McCurdy
Molly McGaan
Chris McGowan
Emma McKee
Jessica McKellar
Patrick & Kara McKenna
Melissa McMahon
Lauren McNamara Phillips
Lester McNeely
Paul Mendoza
Andrew Merrill
Jenna Tine Meyer
Alan Miller
Martha Miller, AICP
Rebecca Millham
Andrea Milne
Katrina Mitchell
Gilad Shanan and Sarah Moberg
Josh Mogerman
Rebeca Mojica
Matthew Mokma
Andrew Mondschein
Brooke Monea
Benjamin Monroe
Scott Moorhouse
Carmelisa Morales
Lindsey Morel
Saul Moreno
Joe Morris
Christina Morrison
James Morrison
Julia Mossbridge
Lauren & Grace M.
Garrett Muller
Anthony Murphy
Rachel Myszak
Ryan Nagle
Jaclyn Nagy

Jim Nance
naomi
Sneha Narayan
Bruce Nelson
Armond Netherly
Mike Kennedy, Magnetic Press
NEXTSTL.com
Nick Ng
Christine Vi Nguyen
Joe Nickence
Corey Nissenberg
Matthew N. Noe
Northside Dermatology
Alexandra Novak
Marisa Novara
Julie A. O'Connor
Steph O'Connor
Colleen O'Leary
Jeanne Marie Olson
Michael Olson
Katharine Ommanney
Kevin Orzel
Jeffrey W Osman
Hunter Owens
Emanuel Padilla
Aaron Paley
Keri Palma
Adam Paradis
Rita Parida
Matt Parker
Jared Patton
Chris Payne
Tom Pearl
Christina Pei
Mark E Penzien
Alea Perez
D.R. (Solo) Perry
Kevin T. Perry, PE, AIA
Alexa Pesmen
Laura Petelle
Bethany Peters
Scott J Petersen
Anne Petersen
JP Petriello
Rachel T. Pham
Eric Pierce
Jarrett Day Pierre
Kris Pierre
Claire Pieterek
Thea, Frank and Max Polancic
Nicholas Poluha
Scarlet Ponder
Erin Potter
Debbie Poulin
Rebecca Poulson
Ellen Power
Kurtis Pozsgay
Marisa Prasse
Charles Proffitt
Project GUTS
Mary Pumphrey
Patrick 'Q' Quilao
David Quinlan
Lisa Quintero
Amanda R
Rachel
Karthik Raja

Vignesh Ram
Red Brick Realty
The Redstick family
Jacqui Reedy
Jennifer Reinhardt
William Rice
Laurie J Rich
Brian Richard
Robert S. Rihtar
Teme Ring
Nathan Ritter
JOSEPH RITTMAN
Derek & Sara Roach
Sam Robbins
Teryn J. Robinson
mig rod
Omar Rodriguez
Shelagh Rodriguez
Erin Roberts
Haley Roeser
Brian Rogers
Lucinda Rogers
Stephanie Rolley
Meliza
Michiko Romm
Mollie Rosario
Jacquelin Rose (JJ)
Hallie Rosen
margaret rosenthal
Drew Roskos
Lucas C. Ross
Forrest & Paula Rossen
Matthew Rossi
Leeatt Rothschild
Matt Rubin
Frank Ruchala
Dan Russell
Kyle Russo
Tony Ruth
Owen Ryan
Victor Saad
Aaron Salmon
Karyn Sandlos
Elisa Sandoval
Bud Santos
Sara
Alfred Saucedo
Sara Scanlan
Lindsey Scannapieco
Alix Scarborough
David Schalliol
Benjamin Schapiro
Timothy R Schmitt
ben schmitz
Tiffany Schmoker
Serena Schreiber
Kevin Schreur
Aaron R. Schroeder
Sage Schroeder
Brian D. Schultz
Michael Schur
Claire Schuster
Nancy E. Schwab
Dorothy Schwankl
Steven Schwartz
Ricki and Alan Schwimmer
Holden Scully
Jeffrey Seastrom
J.J. Sedelmaier

Jesús Segura
Kate Selden
Evan Sellers
Serena
Avner Shanan
arLene Shannon
Steph Shapiro
Stephen Sharp
Michael Shaub
Nate Shaw
Sammi Shay
Hannah Sheehy
The Siegal Family
Eva Silverman
Lou Silverman
Jacob Simanowitz
Alec Singer
Dan Sitton
Laura Sjoquist
Samuel Sklar
Jessica Skocinski
Stephanie Slattery
Claire Smalley
Jennifer Nelson Smid
Jeremy Smith
Lee Smith & Wendy Leopold
Matthew Smith
Nicholas Snavely
Peter E Snyder
Jeff Solin
Soprych Family
Nick Sousanis
Kristi Stainback
Katherine Stalker
Mary Steenson
Jon S. Steindorf
Vance Stevens
Aaron Stigberg
oliviastinson
Travis Stluka
Ian Stockdale
Cristy Stone
Stoney
Lon Stousland
Chuck Strawser
Jeffrey Alan Stvan
Koushik Subramanian
Jennifer Suerth
Claudia Caro Sullivan
Tim Swanson
Josh and Leah Swindler
Lindsey Telford
Billy Terrell
Dhiru A. Thadani
Kairsten Thies
Eileen Thomas
Parker Thomas
Jake Thompson
Thoughtcrime Press
Angela Tillotson
Paige Tobin
Thomas & Lauren Tockey
Anthony R. Todd
Allison Torban
Francesca Torello
Jane Trask
Matt Trewartha

Mrs. Trine
Andrea Trudeau
Jill S. Tuinier
Peter & Katherine Tulloch
Crissy Turino
Benjamin Turner
Erik Turner
Shannon Turner
The Uchida Jensen Family
Sue Uhlig
BJ van Glabbeek
Matthew & Stacey Vanada
Rich E. Vander Klok
Ryan Vaughn
Abril Vela
Eduardo and Paz Velazquez
Katie Verkruyse
David Vessel
M+B+O Villanueva
Jan Wade
Arjun Wadnerkar
Kellen M. Walden
Kristy Wang
Brian Warmoth
Jacob Way
The Weffer Family
Neil Wehrle
Kate and Yishai Weinstein
J. Weisbord
Sandor Weisz
Lynee Wells
Ron & Jill Wheeler
Lauren White
Michael White
Jacqueline Ronan Whitehouse
Josh Whitener
Chris Whittaker
Jennifer Wiemhoff Gruenhagen
Drew Williams-Clark
Tiffany R. Williams
Bess Williamson
David Wilson
Emily E. Wilson
mark wilson
Scott Neal Wilson
Simon Wistow
Anna Wojcik
Anne Wolke
Tina Wong
Wrap Architecture
Gordon Wright
Chris Wuellner
James Wylde
Charlie Young
Tieg Zaharia
Kevin Zakszewski
Tony Zale
Sanja Zehnder
William Zeng
Kristiana Zerom
Ms. Yichen Zhang
Allen Zheng
Andrew Ziegler
Alana ZImmer
Barbara Zubek
Tara Zuber

COLUMN

A. Beckles
Stephanie Duran
Kathryn Duval

Jose "Gigio" Esteras
Nathan Greenstein

Jayem Griffin
Laura Kamedulski
Lee Kuhn

John W. Palmer
Stephanie Pereira
Henry Siegel

James Turnbull
Bradlie Yanniello

BRICK

Sarah Bradley
Brian Downing
Ku Hap
Hereticked

Jacob R Huebner
Mari Lee Kozlowski
Ruth Lang
Mario

Nichari Sitthiwirachtham
Chloe Wandler
Joni Whitworth

*Denotes Gala 2017 supporter

Acknowledgments
From the Authors

From Gabrielle Lyon, Chicago Architecture Foundation

First thanks go to Lynn Osmond for her vision and collaboration on this project.

Thank you to the *Wacker's Manual* Advisory Committee: Ben Leitschuh, American Planning Association; Jessica Marshall, Chicago Public Schools; Shawn Healy, McCormick Foundation; Nathan Mason, Department of Cultural Affairs and Special Events; Jeff McCarter, Free Spirit Media; Shelley Stern-Grach, Microsoft; and Angel Ysaguirre, Illinois Humanities.

Heartfelt thanks to the following for their input and guidance: Charles Adler, Andrew Balster, Jesse Banwart, Zach Border, Jessica Cilella, Jennifer Choi, John DeVries, Rachel DeWoskind, Dan O'Connell, Mindy Faber, Brian Fitzpatrick, Adam Fotos, Vicki Garza, Jenni Groot, Julio Guerrero, Bennett Haller, Tim Harris, Jake Huebner, Julie Jacobson, Janeen Lee, Heidi Lubin, Dennis McClendon, Rashaan Meador, Rebecca Milham, Patrick Miner, Michele Morales, Jim Parsons, Stephanie Periera, Nichole Pinkard, Jay Porter, Ashley Powers, Emmanuel Pratt, Wesley Quevado, Edgar Quintanilla, Shawn Reddy, Liz Robbins, Omar Rodriquez, Stephen Rosado, Andrea Saenz, Brian Schultz, Helen Slade, Steven Slivka, Jeff SOlins, David Stovall, John Syvertsen, John Tolva, Jaimielee Velasquez, Christy Uchida, Eleazar Varquez, Fred Wacker and Jenn Yoo.

Special thanks to Willa Zhang for skilled writing and editorial assistance just in the nick of time.

Devin, Kayce, Chris and Deon: working with Eyes of the Cat Illustration to create *No Small Plans* was an extraordinary privilege.

To current and future Teen Fellows: you inspired this project and kept it "real." This book is by, for and about you.

From Eyes of the Cat Illustration
eyesofthecatillustration.com

Thank you Nina Limbeck, for your endless patience and for keeping Devin well nourished. Special thanks to Barrett Bayer and Brian Bauman for being amazing uncles! Thank you, Lindsay Chenault Bolton, for your gracious computer loan. Thank you, Otis, for grounding Kayce and Chris, and giving them renewed purpose in the fight for a just city and neighborhood. Big thank you to Phillip and Constance Horton for being supportive grandparents, and to Deon's mom—Monica Horton—for blessing him with much needed mental support. Thank you public school students and teachers, especially the scholar-artists of ChiArts for educating us on a daily basis. Finally, a huge humble thanks to everybody out there doing the often boring and usually necessary work to build a better future.